The Family Oops and Burns First Aid

By Kristina Stiles
Illustrated by Jill Latter

In a rickety house down the Smoky Hill Close

Lived the family Oops, whom everyone knows.

Brother and sister, and both parents Oops

Were quite careless with hot things when there was no excuse.

Mummy Oops wore bright lipstick and liked to look good,

She straightened her hair way more than you should.

Without wearing sun cream she sunbathed for hours,

Then red as a beetroot she spent days in cold showers.

Mummy Oops left her straighteners on the back of door handle

And the Little Girl Oops tried to follow mummy's example -

She touched the hot tongs and felt a horrible "OUCH"!

If only Mummy Oops used a heat-resistant straightener pouch.

Daddy Oops loved his tea and an outdoor barbeque

He would boil a kettle and leave it to brew

Baby Oops reached to taste Daddy's favourite drink,

Pulling down the hot liquid in what seemed like a blink.

Days of rain made the barbeque harder to light

So Daddy Oops poured on some special liquid to help it ignit

When his t-shirt caught fire, the firefighters came

And said:

"**STOP**,

COVER your face,

DROP and **ROLL**

to put out the flames."

So the Oops went to school run by **Mrs Coolwalter**

Who taught first aid for burns and the importance of water.

The Oops family listened to Mrs Coolwalter's burns lessons

On what you should do during the first valuable seconds.

Going out in the sun without sun cream or hat,

And touching hot surfaces can hurt rather bad,

Hot water and fire can lead to a burn.

Prevention is key, as the Oops family learned.

Putting toothpaste on burns won't do the trick,

Using egg whites or ice can make you quite sick;

Cream is too thick and butter – too greasy,

Eggs are just eggy and ice is quite freezing.

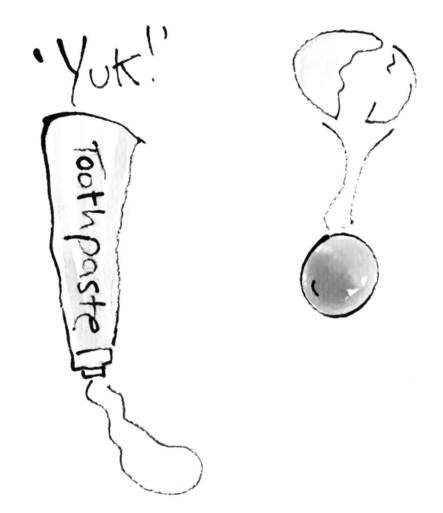

First aid for burns follows four simple steps:

REMOVE, COOL and COVER, then CALL for some help.

Remove nappies, all jewellery and any loose clothing,

As they hold in the heat and stop swelling evolving.

Remove

"*Twenty minutes of cooling under running tap water*

Is the most vital burn treatment!" taught Mrs Coolwalter.

Don't apply frozen peas, any ice or cold fluids

And it may save you a trip to the local burns unit.

Use a loose piece of Cling Film to cover your burn

It will lessen the stingy-sore feeling in turn.

Take some usual medicine to make pain go away

And call for some help with no further delay.

Cover

cling film

The Oops family passed all the tests at the school

And received "First Aid Champion" badges, which did look quite

They proudly showed off their awards to their friends

And shared the first aid message the burns team recommends:

"First aid for burns follows four simple steps:

REMOVE, COOL and COVER, then CALL for some help."

Will Mrs Coolwalter find a new superstar?

I think it'll be you and you will go far!

"Superstar"

Kristina Stiles is
a Mummy to Lily and Sam
– two sparkly rays of sunshine!

Kristina was born in Latvia and came to
the UK to complete her higher education, first
graduating with a BA in Social Psychology and later
– a Diploma in Adult Nursing. Kristina discovered the
burns speciality as a student nurse and has worked as
the Burns Clinical Nurse Specialist for the last 15 years,
passionately championing the burn prevention and first aid
messages through education and awareness campaigns.

The Oops Family story is inspired by two amazing
toddlers with nearly identical scald burns who had
very different first aid treatments at the time of
injury resulting in very different outcomes.

This story is dedicated to many
families like theirs, who are
brave every day.